The Big Book of
LIMERICKS
(to laugh at)

The Big Book of
LIMERICKS
(to laugh at)

Written and Illustrated by
EDWARD S. MULLINS

PLATT & MUNK/*Publishers*
NEW YORK

Published in New York by The Platt & Munk Co., Inc.
Distributed simultaneously in Canada by Nelson, Foster & Scott Limited.
All rights reserved.
Printed and bound in Japan.
Library of Congress Catalog Card Number: 77-75890

To Mary

Columbus set sail without fear
On the seaworthy Santa Maria,
  But he mumbled, while tossing
  On a very rough crossing,
"Oh dear, I hope India's near."

Said an elephant lady who poses,
"My beautiful cheeks are like roses,
But it's true that I get
A little upset
When they talk about cute little noses."

Little Jenny wore pants like her brother,
And Bill had long hair like his mother.
What with bracelets and rings
And some other bright things,
You couldn't tell one from the other.

Said the bird to the bull, partly teasing,
"That ring in your nose is most pleasing."
Said the bull, all aglow,
"Yes, it's lovely I know,
But it gets in the way when I'm sneezing."

A boy in Nebraska, one day,
Blew up his balloon the wrong way.
'Stead of out, he blew in,
The balloon remained thin,
But the lad up and floated away.

The very first wheel, I declare,

Was invented by Shamus O'Hare.

And it's certain that Shamus

Might well have been famous

If he'd made his wheel round and not square.

Mrs. Hippo, who purchased a drape,
Made it into a beautiful cape.
"It's a bargain," said she,
"But the best part, to me,
Is how nicely it flatters my shape."

Out dining, a young alligator,
When asked if he'd have coffee later,
　　Just shook his large head,
　　and pleasantly said,
"I was planning on having the waiter."

Said a jolly young goldfish named Lear
Upon kissing his mate on the ear,
    "Have you ever detected
    Or even suspected
That it's not very private in here?"

A bunny, as cute as can be,

Was put in the shade of a tree,

But he melted away

In the heat of the day.

(He was made out of chocolate, you see.)

A scarecrow employed to scare crows,
Was given some ragged old clothes.
       He said, "Why should I wear 'em,
       When nothing will scare 'em?
They're sitting in rows on my nose!"

A field mouse was chased through the wet
By a cat with a butterfly net.
    The cat slipped and sweated
    And got himself netted,
And the mouse took him home for a pet.

A snake charmer, earning his keep,
Played notes that were mellow and deep,
Till the snake raised his head
And quietly said,
"Play faster, I'm falling asleep!"

At the animal masquerade dance,
The lion appeared in short pants,
While the elephant twins,
Wearing very broad grins,
Came dressed as a couple of ants.

"I can't move," shouted Bill to his brother.
"Perhaps we had better call Mother!"
Said his brother to Billy,
"You really are silly!
Your shoe-strings are tied to each other."

There was a young woman from Wales
Who complained, after eating some snails,
"They slip down with a glide,
But once deep inside,
They go right on a-waggin' their tails."

A very courageous baboon
Wrote home on his way to the moon,
"The trip is quite nice,
But take my advice—
Don't *ever* come up by balloon!"

What's purple and shaped like a bear
With masses of long, curly hair?
The answer, of course,
Isn't cow, bird, or horse,
But a purplish, curly-haired bear.

Said his wife to an old man from Garms,
"Your clothing is one of your charms,
　　But you've done something wrong,
　　For your sleeves are too long."
(He was wearing his pants on his arms!)

Said a bird in a cage, "Lady Fair,
Let's escape and enjoy the fresh air."
Said his cute little mate,
"Perhaps we should wait.
There's a cat that looks hungry out there!"

A very fat snow-man named Wheezer
Was truly a clever old geezer.
Whenever he felt
He was starting to melt,
He'd spend a few days in the freezer.

A witch who haunted town fairs
Had been bragging and putting on airs.
But last Halloween,
She was not even seen.
Her broom was garaged for repairs.

A girl on the flying trapeze,
Going through her performance with ease,
Was suddenly frozen.
Her partner had chosen
A terrible moment to sneeze.

In Venice, the delicate hues
Of the skies and canals are soft blues.
But when going for rides
On the incoming tides,
Watch out for those leaky canoes.

Said a horse to a pig named McGrubbles,
"Being dirty's your greatest of troubles.
    Here's some soap," said the horse.
    The pig ate it, of course,
Then had fun all day long blowing bubbles.

Now here's a most interesting riddle:
What's brown with a hole in the middle?
    A doughnut? Why no!
    I was sure you would know.
The answer, of course, is a fiddle!

A cute little beaver named Sam
Was building a beautiful dam.
From their house, sister Sue
Shouted "Sam, where are you?"
Answered Sam, from the dam, "Here I am!"

A submarine captain named Fleck
Had a terrible cold in his neck.
  Said Dr. McPottit,
  "You probably got it
While walking around on the deck."

An old Saint Bernard who could paint,
When asked, "Are you really a saint?"
    Started in to reply
    When his wife, with a sigh,
Said, "A saint he most certainly ain't!"

An elephant, quite at his ease,
Asked his girl for a kiss and a squeeze.
  She was very polite
  So she answered, "All right,
But watch out with those tusks, if you please."

An echo repeats things with ease—ease—ease

You can make it repeat what you please—please—please.

But, one echo I know

Who, when I say "Hello,"

Always answers me back with a sneeze—sneeze—sneeze.

A honey bee, busy and buzzy,

All yellow and black and quite fuzzy,

    Can make honey, I know—

    I've been told this is so—

But what *I'd* like to know is, how does he?

A lady from Kansas named Shore,
While reducing, lost pounds by the score.
Her husband, one night,
Had a horrible fright
When she slipped through a crack in the floor.

"If man," said a fellow from Bimini,
"Was intended for smoking, by jiminy,
It is clear, one supposes,
That all of our noses
Would be made upside-down like a chiminey."

A language is something you speak,
Like in Greece, they speak mainly in Greek.
In Japan, Japanese,
And in China, Chinese,
(And in Mouseville, of course, it's a squeak.)

A dog asked a snake who seemed chummy
If, when crawling, he got his chin crummy.
    Said the snake, looking sad,
    "On the chin it's not bad,
But it's terribly rough on the tummy."

"My teeth," said a shark up in Flushing,
"Are terrific for munching and crushing.
They're so sharp and so white,
And so beautifully bright,
Because I spend hours just brushing."

An Eskimo Mr. and Mrs.
Rub noses as we would give kisses.
When told what they're missing
By not trying kissing,
They said, "You should see how nice *this* is."

"Mr. Mink," said a curious mole,
"What, in life, is your ultimate goal?"
Said the mink, on the spot,
"My goal, sir, is *not*
To end up as a coat or a stole."

When you notice how fragrant a rose is,
And how lovely the smell of clean clothes is—
When the scent of spring trees
Drifts along on the breeze,
Then you know how important a nose is.

A handsome young dog named McDoodles
Fell in love with the nicest of poodles.
    Said this poodle, named Dot,
      "Do you love me a lot?"
Said McDoodles, "Just oodles and oodles!"

Said an ant who had traveled the land,
And seen castles and palaces grand,
"I think it's just peachy,
Lying here where it's beachy,
A-wiggling my toes in the sand."

A ventriloquist's dummy, named Bright
Thought his boss wasn't talking just right.
He said, "How would it be
If you sit on *my* knee,
And *I'll* do the talking tonight!"

It's true what they say about France.
It's really the land of romance.
On the banks of the Seine,
When it starts in to rain,
Policemen all line up and dance.

Said a horse to his blushing young bride,
"Let us gallop through life side-by-side.
    We'll work hard on Monday,
    But then every Sunday
We'll go for a people-back ride."

The Antarctic, all covered with snow,
Is hardly a place I would go,
    But it's heaven to whales,
    Coolly slapping their tails.
(They're very slap-happy, you know.)

Miss Grover, a maiden from Dover,
Wore a bonnet with dyed purple clover.
'Twas a beautiful flower,
But, when caught in a shower,
Miss Grover got purple all over.

Said I to a fly, "It's so scaring
To walk upside-down with such daring."
    Said the fly from the ceiling,
    With a smile most appealing,
"It's these triple-grip sneakers I'm wearing."

An artist whose leg was in traction
Was suddenly worn to distraction.
Feeling weary and faint,
He jumped in the paint,
And came up like a crazy abstraction.

When one of those cute little llamas,
Dressed up in some fancy pajamas,
Spilled milk on the knee,
He was scared as could be.
The pajamas, you see, were his mama's!

A chick who was learning to fly
Said, "Papa, I'd rather not try."
   Asked the rooster, "Why, pray,
   Are you acting this way?"
And she said, " 'Cause I'm chicken, that's why!"

Uncle Harry is so good at rowing,
That huffing and puffing and blowing,
He gets moving so fast
As he goes flying past
He meets himself coming and going.

In buying a camel that's new,
And in buying one second-hand, too,
The salesman says, "Sir,
Tell me which you prefer,
A model with one hump or two?"

Said an octopus fellow named Andy,
When asked if eight arms were unhandy,
"There are times, I suppose,
As when buying my clothes,
But for waiting on tables they're dandy!"

Said a bird to his friend from the West,

"That's a beautiful bright-colored vest."

Said his friend, in reply,

With pride in his eye,

"Don't be silly, you goose, that's my chest."

A pretty young lady named Grace
Had powder all over her face.
When someone asked why,
She could only reply,
"It seemed the most logical place."

There was an old man from St. Paul
Who had practically no hair at all.
    A fly on his head
    Thought sure he'd be dead
When he skidded and had a bad fall.

In a circus parade in South Norbit,
A very strong drummer named Corbit
Threw his stick in the air.
It went heaven knows where,
But I'm told it's now flying in orbit.

Said the bear to the dog, "You're so pale!
Oh, why do you sob so and wail?"
Said the dog to the bear,
"Perhaps you don't care,
But you're standing, old boy, on my tail."

A parachute jumper named Rupp
Told his pupil, a rather dull pup,
    "The next time you jump
    You'll get less of a bump
If you open your parachute up."

An intelligent earthworm named Fred
Invented a game, and he said,
   "Who wins and who loses
   Depends on who chooses
Which end is my tail or my head."

A maiden from over the seas
Wore clothes that were made of sweet peas.
    She really looked fine
    And smelled quite divine
But was *constantly* bothered by bees.

A photographer's helper named Crane,
Taking mountain-top pictures in Spain,
Stepped back for a shot
Of a picturesque spot,
And never was heard from again.

Old Rover, a highly trained pet,
Climbed a tree to get out of the wet.
When asked to descend,
He said, "Sorry, my friend,
They just haven't taught me that yet."

A girl from New Jersey named Rhoda,
On tasting her first chocolate soda,
Thought it tasted so great,
She had seven or eight.
It was nearly enough to explode her.

The African jungles are scary,
And full of things squealy and hairy.
So try to have fun,
But be ready to run
If you're out on a jungle safari.

A two-headed dragon beside me,
Said sadly as soon as he spied me,
"This fire-breathing I do
May seem great fun to you
But think how it heats what's inside me."

Mr. Smith who has traveled in Chile
Insists that it's perfectly silly,
　　Since the morning he got there,
　　Was terribly hot there,
To imagine that Chile is chilly.

A kangaroo mother, quite grand,
Went to shop at a vegetable stand.
When a pick-pocket came,
Her baby, named Mame,
Took a bite of the pick-pocket's hand.

In his pool, when a high-diving otter
Dove in to show off for his daughter,
    He started to frown
    When half the way down,
He noticed they'd drained out the water.

There once was a funny old chap
Who sat with a dog in his lap.
When he quickly stood up,
The clever young pup
Jumped higher and sat on his cap.

Said a centipede mother of nine,
"Having this many children is fine,
But it's really no joke,
And it's keeping me broke
Buying shoes for a family like mine."

Mrs. Smith gave her hippo a tap
And sent him upstairs for his nap.
Said the lady, perspiring,
"It's terribly tiring
To hold him all day on my lap."

A hornbill who lives in La Paz
Does his best with whatever he has.
A parrot can speak,
But, because of his beak,
The hornbill can only play jazz.

While watching TV, a Miss Fox,
Remarked to her friend, Mrs. Cox,
"I don't know, I'll admit,
How those people can fit
Inside of that one little box."

Sylvester, a hound dog from Leicester,

Who was really a clown and a jester,

Had a nose like a fig,

And his tail was so big

That, believe me, the tail wagged Sylvester.

"Here, waiter!" cried old Mr. Browning.

"A fly's in my soup," he said, frowning.

Said the waiter, "Oh, sir!

Must we stand and confer

While that poor fly is certainly drowning?"

At ninety, old Mr. McWort
Took basketball up as a sport.
But the coach shook his head.
"I'm sorry," he said,
"I'm afraid you're a little too short."

A gnu who escaped from the zoo,
But returned in an hour or two,
Said "I'm telling you boys,
All that traffic and noise
Is too much for a gnu to go through."

King Arthur insisted each knight
Should be very correct and polite.
Every morning at dawning
Each knight said "good morning"
And each knight said "good-night" every night.

A monkey, dressed up for a show,
Said, "I can't stand this outfit, you know.
I'll put up with the shirt,
And the shoes, though they hurt,
But that polka-dot tie has to go!"

A little old lady named Brown
Shook her head and declared with a frown,
　　"It's no use in talkin',
　　I'm too old for walkin'!"
Now she roller-skates all over town.

A fellow from Boston named Lance
Couldn't walk well or run well or dance.
 It troubled his mind
 Till he happened to find
That his necktie was caught in his pants.

A bear cub, too tired to play,
Decided to call it a day.
So he fastened the lock,
Then wound up his clock
And set it for quarter-past May.